Glamorous Pumpkin

Phidal

Pumpkin's Poses

Cinderella's precious pet loves to show off her perfect poses and moves. Match your stickers to the shadows to see Pumpkin in action.

1

2 Stretching

Sitting

3

4 Raised Paw

Standing

6

5 Running

The Royal Count

Pumpkin adores glamorous things! Match your stickers to the shadows to see how many of each royal item she has found in the palace.

Party Puppy

Glamorous Pumpkin loves looking her best. Match your stickers to the shadows to see the things she uses when she's getting ready for a royal ball.

Palace Garden

The palace garden is a magical place! Bring this scene to life by adding Cinderella, Pumpkin, Bibbidy, and their woodland friends.

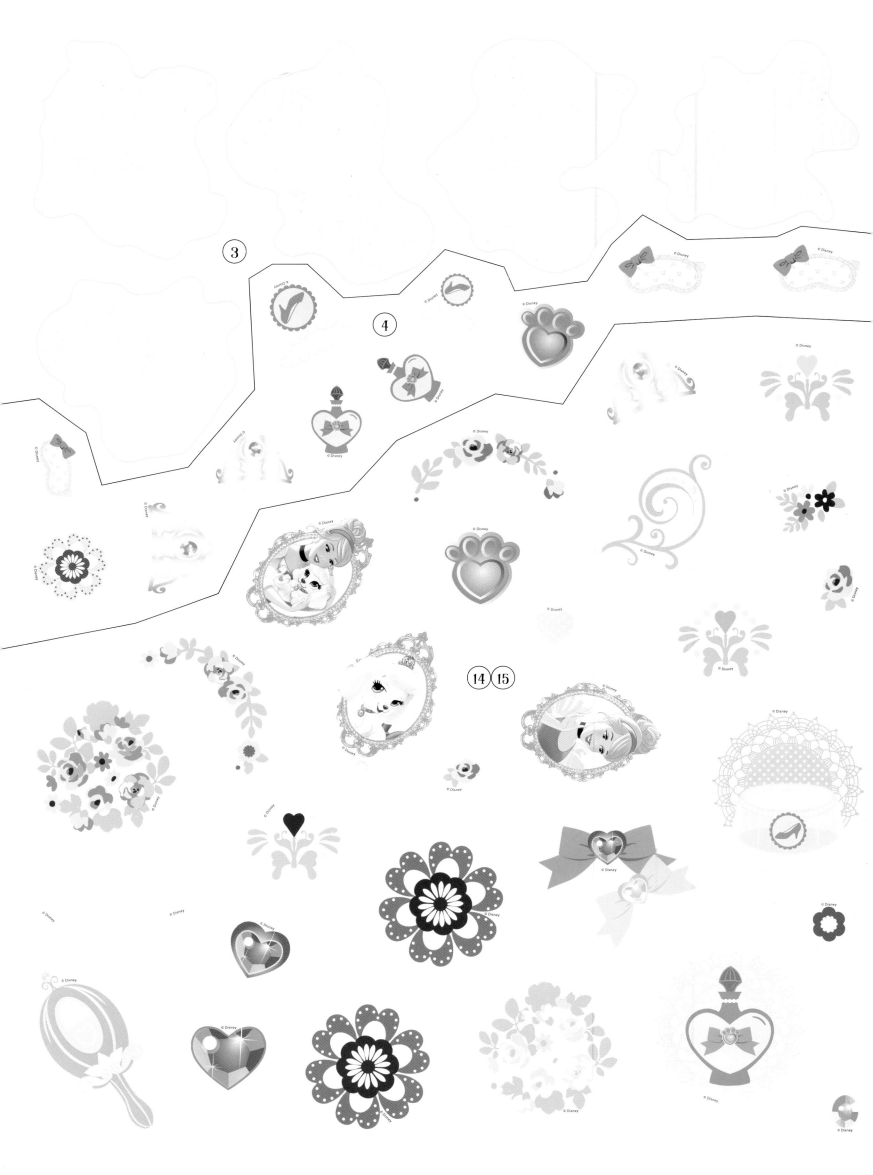

Gem Collection

Pumpkin loves glittery gems of all shapes and colors. Match your stickers to the shadows to complete each row.

Dancing Diva

From the moment Pumpkin was born, all she wanted to do was dance! Use your stickers to discover where Pumpkin loves to dance.

In the Palace Ballroom

In the Royal Coach

On Cinderella's Bed

On the Village Bridge

In the Palace Garden

Pretty Patterns

Pumpkin adores all the beautiful things in the royal palace! Use your stickers to complete the patterns below.

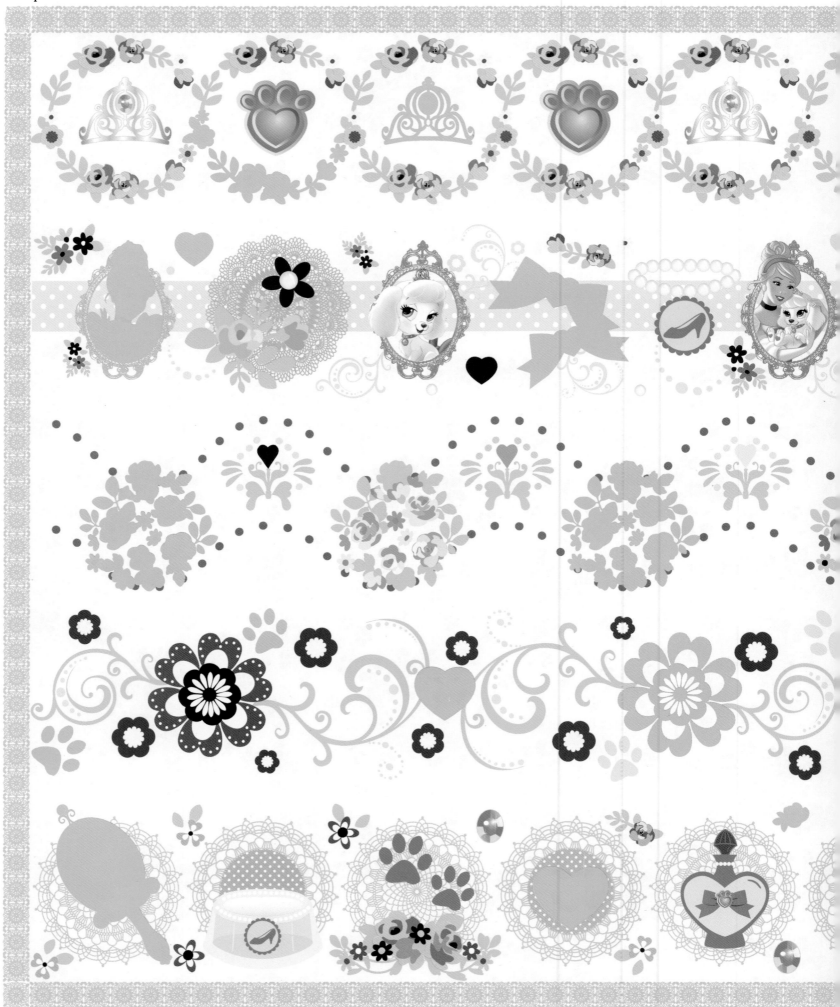

Precious Pair

Pumpkin is Cinderella's precious pet! This elegant puppy would rather be in no one else's arms! Use your stickers to complete the puzzle.

Palace Pets

Sweet Berry

Phidal

Sweet Bunny

Not only is Berry sweet, she adores anything that is sweet! Match your stickers to the shadows to see what other sweet things she loves.

Sweet Berries

Sweet Dreams

Sweet Princess

Hide-and-Seek

Berry and Snow White love playing hide-and-seek in the woods. Find their woodland friends and sweet treats, and then place your stickers on them.

Berry Opposite

Berry is curious about opposites, so Snow White is giving her some examples. Match your stickers to the shadows to learn about opposites.

Running

Inside

Outside

Still

Together

Alone

Standing

Hot

Cold

Sitting

Hippity-Hop

Berry the bunny is hopping around the palace flower garden! There are so many things to hop on and over! Decorate the scene with your stickers.

Sweet Pastime

Berry and Snow White are enjoying a game of tic-tac-toe. Find a friend, and you can play a game of tic-tac-toe too.

12

One of a Kind

Every Palace Pet is unique in his or her look. Match your stickers to the shadows to see some of Berry's special features and accessories.

Castle Counting

There are so many things in and around the castle! Place your stickers on the shadows, and then count the things in each row.

Snowy Bunny

Berry's fluffy white fur coat keeps her warm while she plays in the snow. Match your stickers to the missing puzzle pieces to complete the image.

Palace Pets

Sleepy Beauty

Phidal

Sleepyhead

Summer, fall, winter, or spring... Beauty loves to take naps any time of year! Match your stickers to the shadows in each of the seasonal scenes.

Summer

Fall

Winter

Spring

Can You Guess?

Beauty and Aurora have hidden some of Beauty's things under the great palace rug. Use your stickers to see what they hid.

Sweet Garden Slumber

Beauty likes to nap in the palace garden–just like she was doing when Aurora first found her!
Make the bottom scene look like the top one.

Playfully Pink

Aurora loves to watch Beauty's pink fur shimmer in the sunlight as she chases butterflies in the rose garden. Decorate the scene with your stickers.

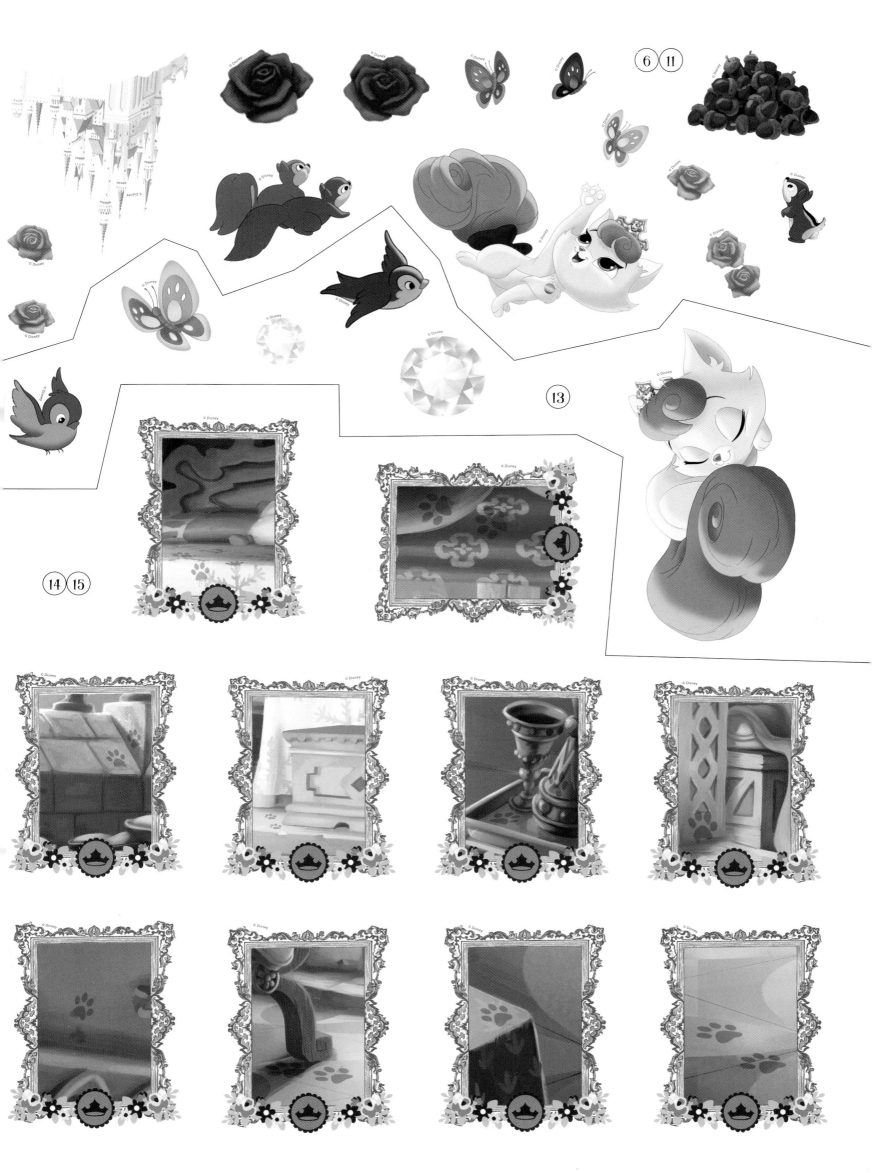

Heavenly Scent

Beauty loves fragrant flowers. Their sweet scent always makes her feel sleepy! Decorate the beautiful bouquet with your stickers.

Land of Play

Although Beauty may spend a lot of time sleeping, she certainly plays a lot in her dreams. Use your stickers to see who and what she is playing with.

Fancy Footprints

After some sweet slumber, Beauty stretched and strolled around Aurora's room. Match your stickers to the rectangles to see where she has been.

Picture Window

The palace has many stained glass windows. This one shows Beauty surrounded by flowers and spirals. Complete the picture with your stickers.

Palace Pets

Prancing Blondie

Phidal

Beautiful Blondie

Blondie loves to trot around the palace garden. Look at each scene, and then use your stickers to make the side-by-side scenes match.

Sweet Summer

Rapunzel's kitten loves accessorizing her look with flowers and trinkets. Match your stickers to the shadows to complete Summer's look.

Parade Pony

This bright-eyed beauty always looks her best for parades! Match your stickers to the shadows to have a closer look at Blondie's decorations.

Sunny Day

Rapunzel, Summer, and Blondie enjoy taking walks together. They love to feel the warm sunshine on their shimmering locks. Decorate the scene.

Bingo!

Blondie and Summer are playing color bingo! Use your stickers to sort out the different colored shapes, and complete each color row on the cards.

Shapes to sort out

A Royal Necklace

Rapunzel is decorating a necklace for Blondie. She's using sparkly gems, shiny gold medals, and silver studs. Use your stickers to help her finish the job!

Enchanted Counting

Blondie, Summer, and Rapunzel love visiting the old tower in the forest. Use your stickers to see who and what there is one of, and what there are many of in this enchanting scene.

Many

One

Regal Friends

These golden-haired gals are the best of friends! Use your stickers to fill in the missing puzzle pieces to make a perfect picture.

Best Friends

Charming Teacup

Phidal

Where is my Cup?

Teacup can't put on a show for Belle without her cup! Place your stickers on the matching shadows to help her find her way to her cup.

Start

Finish

Pretty Petit

Ever since Belle rescued Petit on a cold winter's day, this pony always has a comfortable castle to return to after one of her adventures. Match your stickers to the shadows.

A Performer's Collection

This dancing puppy loves to have props for her shows. Use your stickers to help her sort out her breakable props from her non-breakable ones.

Non-breakable

Breakable

Happy Together

Belle, Teacup, and Petit are so happy that they found each other! They're playing together in Belle's royal bedroom! Decorate the scene with your stickers.

Royal Teacup

When Belle first brought Teacup home, she wanted to repair this performing puppy's broken teacup. Use your stickers to fix and decorate the cup!

Precious Pairs

Belle loves spending time with her two pets! Match your stickers to the shadows to see two of each of the pet poses!

Forest Fun

Teacup, Petit, Belle, and their woodland friends are set to enjoy a storybook together before filling their basket with wildflowers. Use your stickers to make everyone appear in the scene.

Sweet Star

Teacup is not only talented, but also very sweet. She's always eager to show off her perfect training and bat her eyes for Belle. Match your stickers to the missing puzzle pieces to complete the picture.

Palace Pets

Adventurous Treasure

Phidal

Ready for Action

Treasure has a great sense of adventure! She's always looking for additions to her collection of precious trinkets. Use your stickers to see her latest finds.

Up Close

Royal life is filled with beautiful things! Look at each of the close-ups, and then match your stickers to the shadows to reveal the bigger pictures.

Seafaring Kitten

Unlike most cats, Treasure simply adores going to the ocean! This precious pet even loves to make sandcastles. Decorate each sandcastle with the right colored stickers.

Time for a Rest

Although both Ariel and Treasure are always ready for the next adventure, sometimes they need to rest! Decorate Ariel's bedroom with your stickers.

Pretty Pattern

Life wouldn't be the same for Treasure if she couldn't be with her princess, Ariel! Match your stickers to the shadows to complete the pattern.

Color Match

Treasure is sorting her shell collection. She's grouping together similarly colored shells. Use your stickers to help her pair up the shells.

A Royal Cat's Life

This kitten may have an adventurous spirit, but she also loves being a pampered pet. Match your stickers to the shadows to get a peak into her palace life.

Treasure has a
royal meal bowl.

This pretty brush is
for her red fur.

She has a special bow
for special occasions.

Treasure's collar is perfect
for a precious pet!

Just like Ariel, she gets
to wear a tiara!

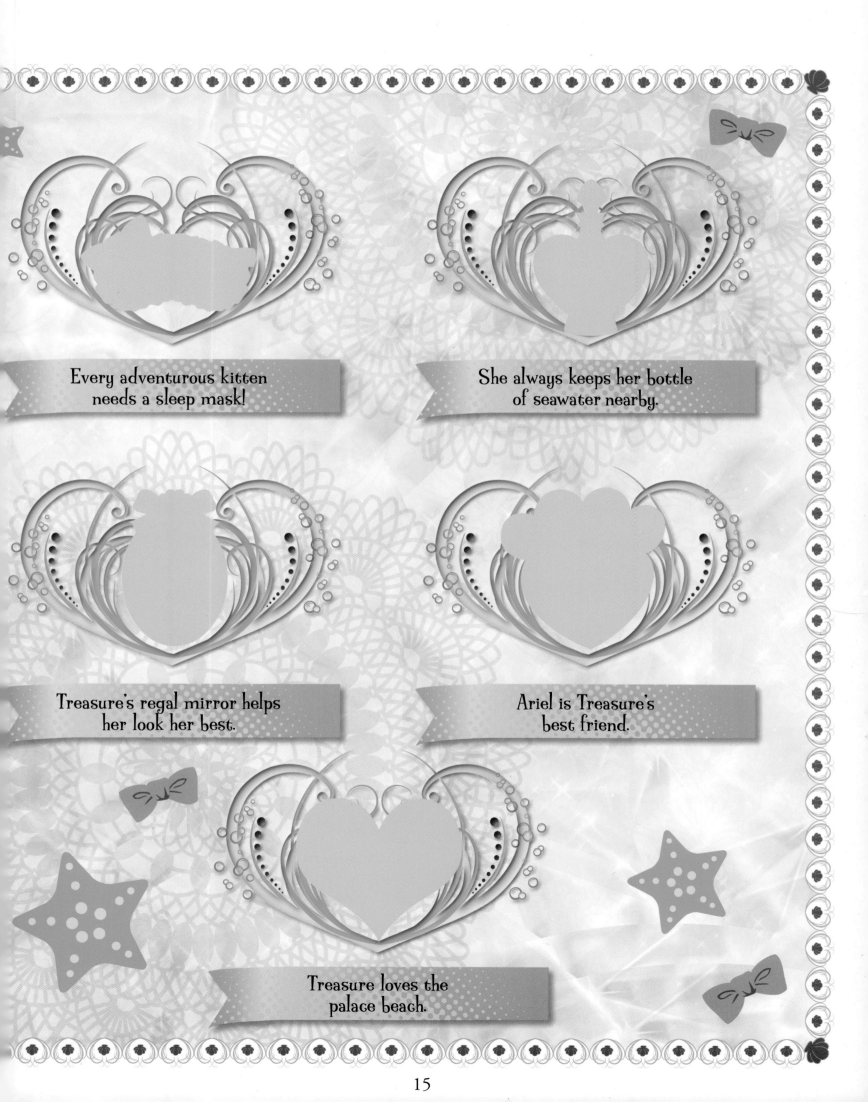

Every adventurous kitten
needs a sleep mask!

She always keeps her bottle
of seawater nearby.

Treasure's regal mirror helps
her look her best.

Ariel is Treasure's
best friend.

Treasure loves the
palace beach.

Curious Kitty

Treasure is playfully exploring the shoreline. She might even decide to go in for a dip! Use your puzzle piece stickers to complete this evening scene.